LEARN TOGETHER

MATHS 2

Hundreds, tens and units; adding in 50s; written problems

Sandra Soper

A Piccolo Original
Piccolo Books

Notes for Parents

The aim of this book is to encourage your child to do maths at home. A great deal will be picked up from your attitude to the work, so when you have time, talk with your child about each activity before you start. Children learn a lot from such conversation and because of it, many mistakes and misunderstandings can be avoided. When a mistake does happen, use it as a learning point rather than a reason for criticism. If you are over-critical, you could put the child off the work altogether. Praise when you can but when there is obviously a lack of effort, say so. Children respect honesty.

In this series we encourage the learning of multiplication tables by heart. It is very useful for the child to have a sound working knowledge of these tables and learning by heart is one way towards this understanding.

Circle every 4th number, then read the circled numbers aloud.
Complete the four times table and learn it by heart.

1	2	3	④	5	6	7	⑧	9	10
11	12	13	14	15	16	17	18	19	20
21	22	23	24	25	26	27	28	29	30
31	32	33	34	35	36	37	38	39	40
41	42	43	44	45	46	47	48	49	50
51	52	53	54	55	56	57	58	59	60
61	62	63	64	65	66	67	68	69	70
71	72	73	74	75	76	77	78	79	80
81	82	83	84	85	86	87	88	89	90
91	92	93	94	95	96	97	98	99	100

$4 \times 1 =$

$4 \times 2 =$

$4 \times 3 =$

$4 \times 4 =$

$4 \times 5 =$

$4 \times 6 =$

$4 \times 7 =$

$4 \times 8 =$

$4 \times 9 =$

$4 \times 10 =$

Draw a triangle round each number which is an answer in the four
times table. Cross out those numbers which are not in the four
times table.

14	24	30	36	12	6
4	15	18	16	8	40
9	16	19	20	32	28

Colour 1 set of 4 steps in column 1, 2 sets in column 2, and so on to finish the 4 times table graph.

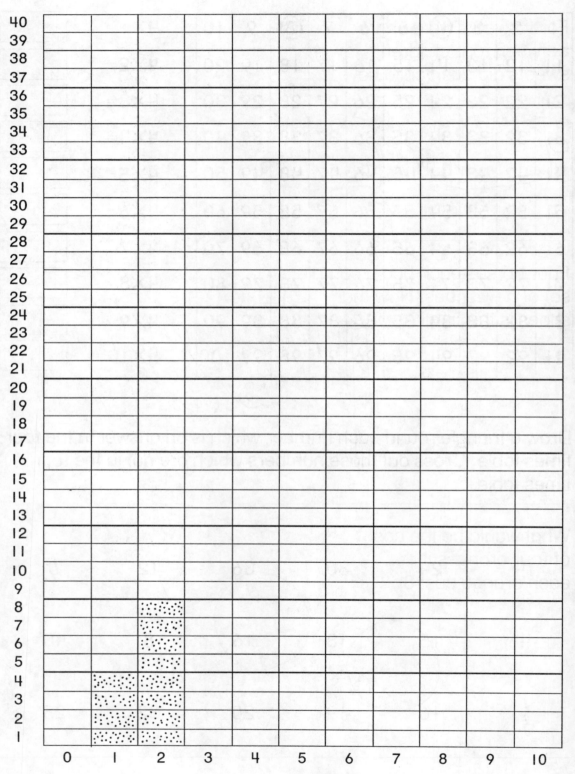

Write a sentence to answer these questions, then colour the pictures.

Forty sweets were shared equally between four children. How many sweets did each child have?

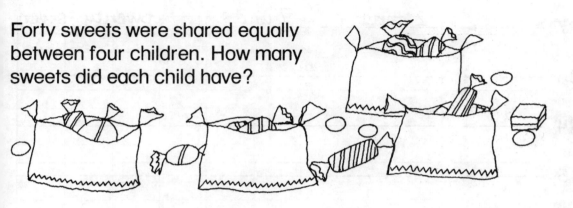

Four horses each had a complete set of new shoes. How many shoes is this in all?

What would be the cost of four oranges if each orange cost 8p?

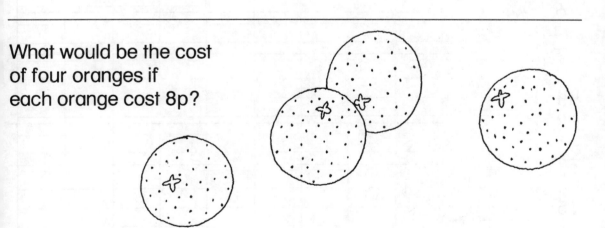

Write these numbers as tens and units. Then write the number in words.

27 ⟶ 2 tens   7 units   twenty-seven

36 ⟶ _____ _____ _____

44 ⟶ _____ _____ _____

15 ⟶ _____ _____ _____

53 ⟶ _____ _____ _____

Say the sum aloud, write the answers, then write the whole sum in words. Can you write the same sum in a different way?

27
−7
20
⟶ Twenty-seven take away seven is twenty.

Seven from twenty seven leaves twenty.

36
−6
___
⟶ _____

_____

44
−4
___
⟶ _____

_____

15
−5
___
⟶ _____

_____

Say these sums aloud in as many different ways as you can. Remember always to start at the units side when working out the answers.

16	32	15	19	20
−4	−20	−12	−18	−10
——	——	——	——	——

66	90	47	78	84
−35	−80	−21	−33	−44
——	——	——	——	——

Read this story, then circle the sum above which tells this story in numbers.

Polly baked fifteen cakes.
Twelve of the cakes were
eaten at tea time. Three cakes
were left on a plate.

Make up a story to show another of the sums above.

Cross out the old price and write in the reduced price. Colour the lamps.

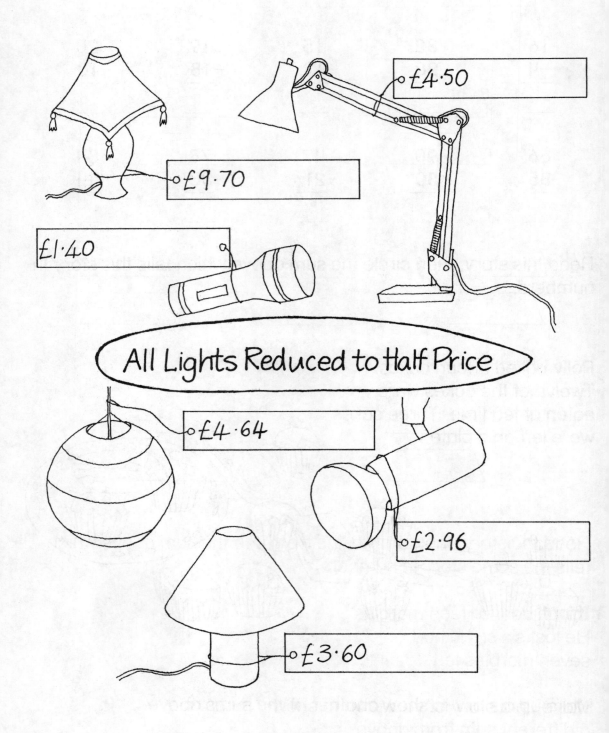

£4·50

£9·70

£1·40

All Lights Reduced to Half Price

£4·64

£2·96

£3·60

Write the answer to each subtraction sum, then write the matching addition sum for each one.

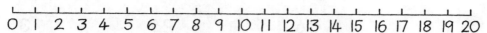

$19-8=11$ $11+8=19$ $17-4=$

$16-7=$ $15-8=$ $13-6=$

$12-9=$ $20-3=$

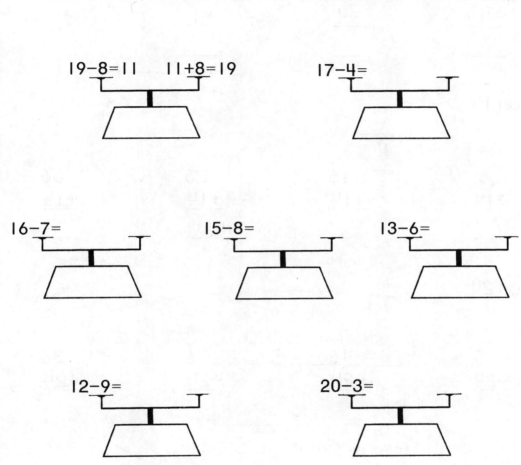

Read the story, then draw a line from it to the sum above which tells the same story in numbers.

Imran had thirteen marbles.
He lost six so he had
seven marbles left.

Make up a story of your own to show
a different sum from above.

9

Add on 4.

6	16	26	36
+4	+4	+4	+4
___	___	___	___

Add on 14.

6	16	26	36
+14	+14	+14	+14
___	___	___	___

Add on 24.

6	16	26	36
+24	+24	+24	+24
___	___	___	___

Read the story, then circle the sum above which tells the same story in numbers.

Twenty-six children went out to play in the playground. Soon four more children came out. Altogether there were thirty children in the playground.

Make up another story to show a different sum from above.

Write the sum in numbers in the box beside each story.

Peter had twenty-four nuts.
When he had given eight
of them to his sister
he had sixteen nuts left.

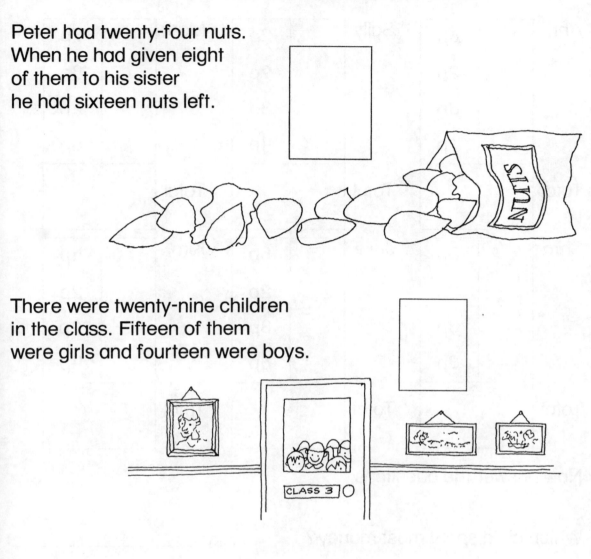

There were twenty-nine children
in the class. Fifteen of them
were girls and fourteen were boys.

Joy used four strips of
coloured paper to decorate
a box. Each strip measured
four centimetres which is
sixteen centimetres altogether.

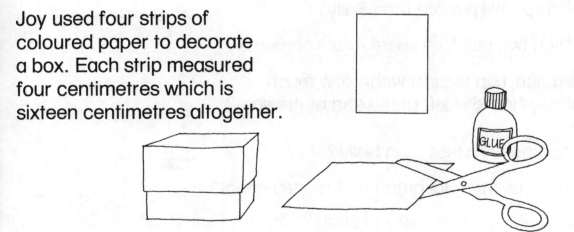

Write the total amount spent by each child at the Jumble Sale.

Ann	
	6p
	2p
	3p
	1p
Total	

Sally	
	2p
	9p
	3p
	4p
Total	

Mark	
	7p
	3p
	2p
	5p
Total	

Shiraz	
	3p
	3p
	3p
	3p
Total	

Julie	
	5p
	2p
	3p
	6p
Total	

Kim	
	4p
	2p
	9p
	4p
Total	

Now answer the questions.

Which child spent most money? _____

Who spent 1p more than Sally? _____

Which two children spent equal amounts? _____

Ann had 15p to start with. How much
money had she left at the end of the sale? _____

Who spent 1p less than Sally? _____

What was the total amount of money spent? _____

Add 50 each time to complete the 50 number chain.

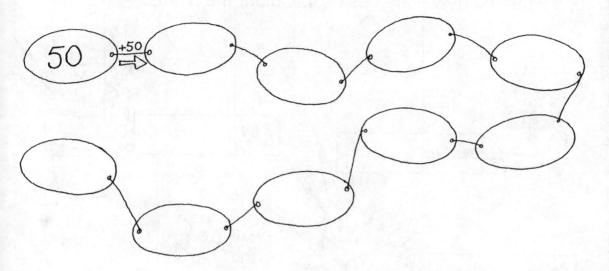

How many fifties are in 100? ☐ 200? ☐ 500? ☐

Write in words.

50 ⟶ _____ 55 ⟶ _____

150 ⟶ _____ 500 ⟶ _____

Add 50 to each number.   Take 50 ⟶

13 ⟶   19 ⟶   500 ⟶

23 ⟶   29 ⟶   450 ⟶

33 ⟶   39 ⟶   400 ⟶

43 ⟶   49 ⟶   350 ⟶

53 ⟶   59 ⟶   300 ⟶

Increase the price of each plant by 50p. Cross out the old price and write the new price beside it. Colour the plants.

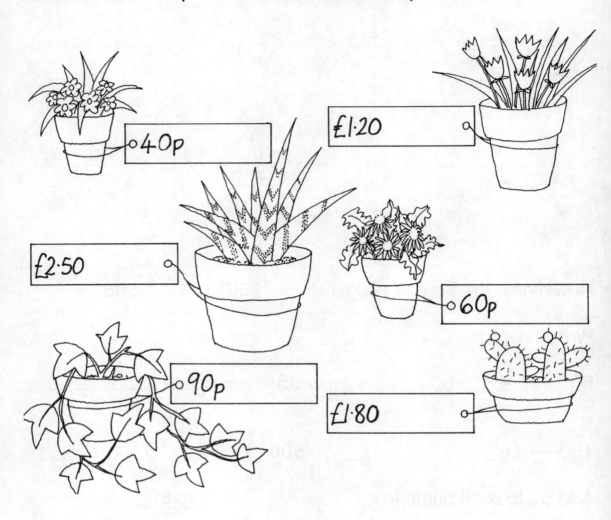

Read the sums aloud, then work out the answers.

h. t. u.	h. t. u.	h. t. u.	h. t. u.
1 2 0	1 4 3	1 2 5	2 5 0
+ 5 0	+ 5 0	+ 5 0	+ 5 0

Fill in the answers in the triangles, then make the scales balance and read the sums aloud.

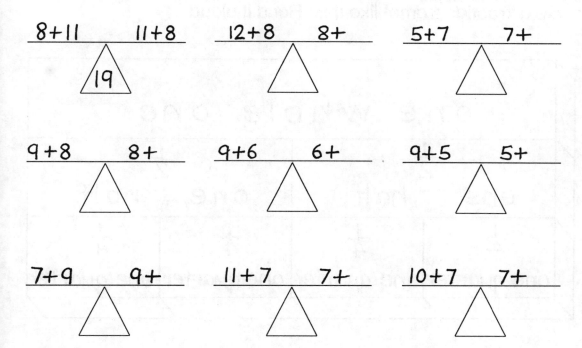

8+11   11+8   12+8   8+   5+7   7+

△ 19

9+8   8+   9+6   6+   9+5   5+

7+9   9+   11+7   7+   10+7   7+

Read the first box along and down, then complete all boxes.

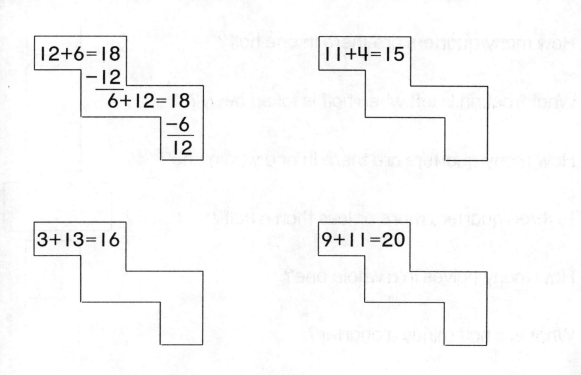

12+6=18
  −12
    6+12=18
      −6
      12

11+4=15

3+13=16

9+11=20

Cover four matchboxes with sticky paper to make 'one whole one', then cover two boxes to make a half etc, to make a 'fraction frame' like this. Read it aloud.

one whole one			
$\frac{1}{2}$ one half		$\frac{1}{2}$ one half	
$\frac{1}{4}$ one quarter	$\frac{1}{4}$ one quarter	$\frac{1}{4}$ one quarter	$\frac{1}{4}$ one quarter

Use the fraction frame to help you to answer the questions.

How many quarters are there in one half?

What fraction is left when half is taken away?

How many quarters are there in one whole one?

Is three quarters more or less than a half?

How many halves in a whole one?

What is a half minus a quarter?

Write a sentence next to each circle to say which fraction is
shaded. Draw a picture using this shape and colour it.

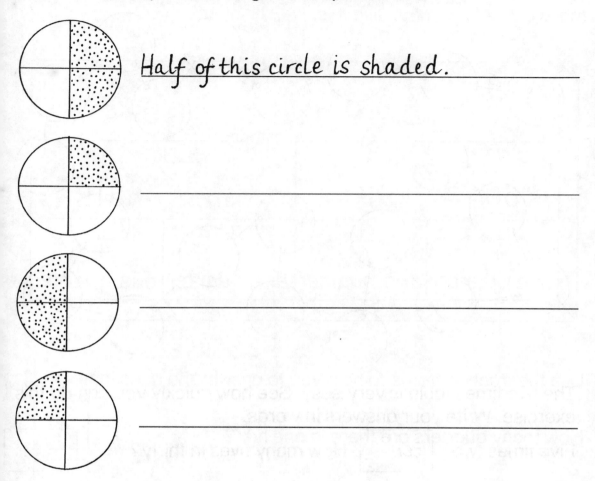

Half of this circle is shaded.

Can you write a sentence for your
answer?

Geoff gave a quarter of his bar
of chocolate to his friend
and a quarter of the bar to his sister.
How much chocolate did Geoff give
away altogether?

Complete the '5 chain' to 100.

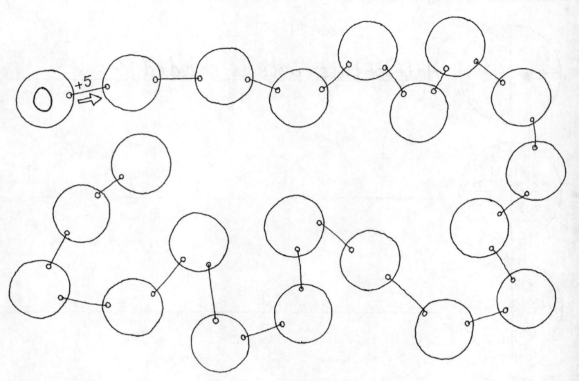

The five times table is very easy. See how quickly you can do this exercise. Write your answers in words.

Five times two | ten | How many fives in thirty? |

Five fours | | Fifty divided by five |

Five sevens | | How many fives in forty? |

Five tens | | How many fives in fifteen? |

Five threes | | Twenty-five divided by five |

Read the first box along and down, then complete all the boxes.

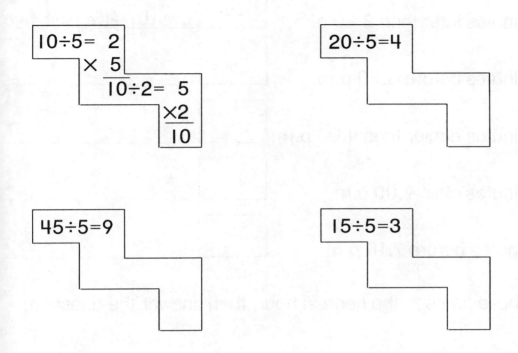

$10 \div 5 = 2$
$\times\ 5$
$10 \div 2 = 5$
$\times 2$
10

$20 \div 5 = 4$

$45 \div 5 = 9$

$15 \div 5 = 3$

Use sticks to show these times on the clock, then colour the clock.

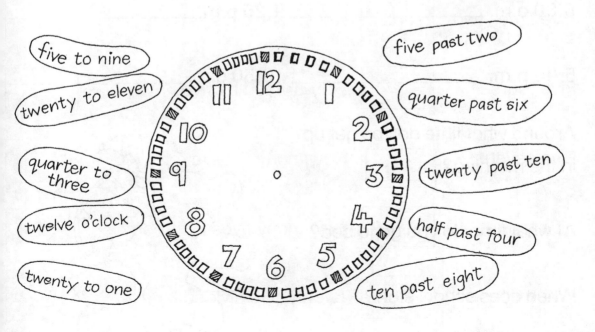

five to nine

twenty to eleven

quarter to three

twelve o'clock

twenty to one

five past two

quarter past six

twenty past ten

half past four

ten past eight

Can you write the time in two ways?

Five minutes later than 2.20 p.m. | 2.25pm | Twenty-five past two

Five minutes before 3.30 p.m.

Five minutes earlier than 4.00 p.m.

Five minutes after 9.00 a.m.

Ten minutes before 7.10 p.m.

Write these times to the nearest hour, then answer the question.

4.15 a.m. _____   6.55 a.m. _____

6.30 a.m. _____   4.25 p.m. _____

5.40 p.m. _____   10.50 a.m. _____

Around what time do you get up
in the morning?

At what time do you go to bed?

When does school start?

Write the difference in the label attached to each box.

100g
40g

The difference
is 60g.

100cm
10cm

£4·50
£5·00

Find the Difference

28 apples
8 apples

4½ hours
5 hours

9 years old
90 years old

Write the missing numbers, then read the table.

6X 1 =

6X = 12

6X 3 =

6X 1 = 24

6X 5 =

6X 6 =

6X = 42

6X =

6X 1 = 54

6X 10 =

Answers to six times table in words.
six

Write the cost.

Six 10p lollipops.

Six 5p balloons.

Six 8p rubbers.

Six 9p cakes.

Six 20p chocolate bars.

Six 2p chews.

Six 50p pens.

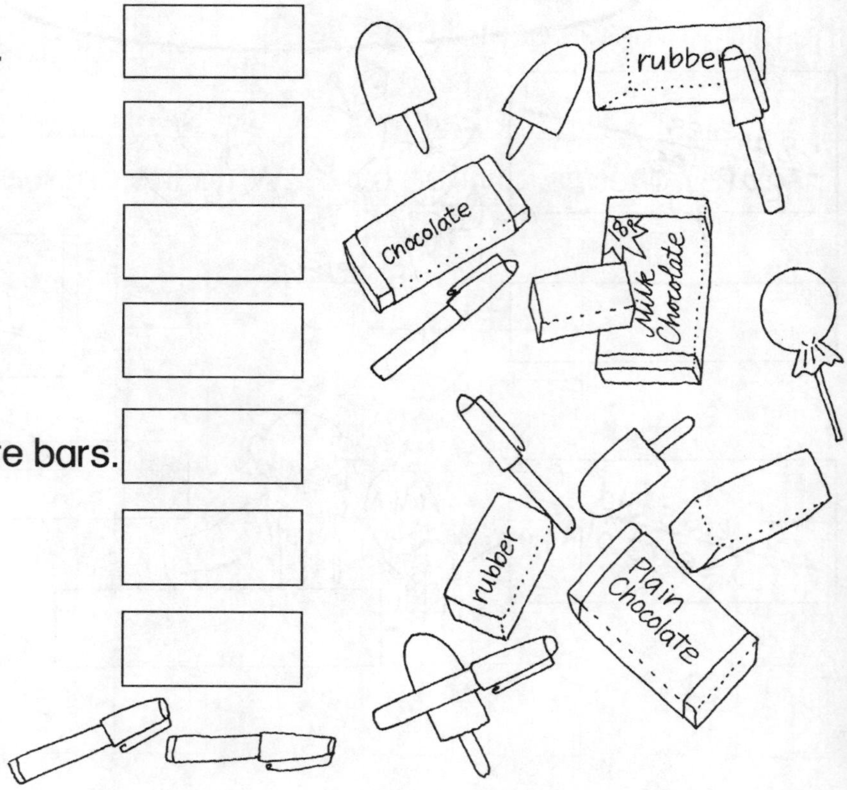

Read the question, then write your answer in a sentence.

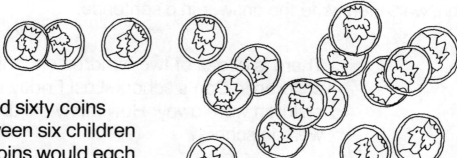

If you divided sixty coins equally between six children how many coins would each child have?

Six children each gave 5p to buy a programme for the concert. How much did the programmes cost altogether?

The arrow means divided by 6. Write the answers in the boxes.

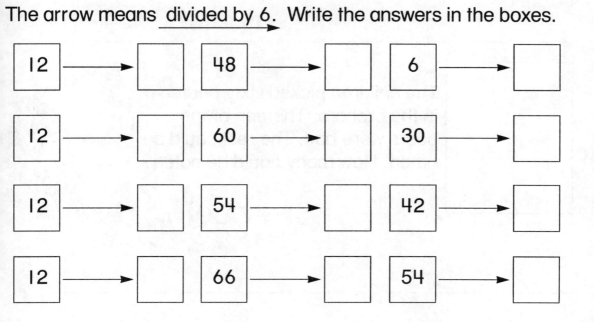

12	→		48	→		6	→	
12	→		60	→		30	→	
12	→		54	→		42	→	
12	→		66	→		54	→	

Read the question. Set out the sum you must do to work out the answer, then write the answer in a sentence.

There is a total of two hundred and thirty children in Dan's school. Last Friday eight children were away. How many children were in school?

Frances had a total of one hundred and twenty-one rubbers in her collection. Julie had collected a hundred and seventeen rubbers. How many more did Frances have than Julie?

The children picked sixty pears in the orchard. Thirteen of the pears were bad. The rest could be eaten. How many could be eaten?

Draw the numbers in the tens and units boxes.

26 ⟶

t	u
o o	● ● ● ● ● ●

39 ⟶

t	u

18 ⟶

t	u

90 ⟶

t	u

51 ⟶

t	u

15 ⟶

t	u

43 ⟶

t	u

66 ⟶

t	u

Write the numbers …   … and the words.

Six tens and one unit.   61   _sixty-one_____

Four tens and five units.   [ ]   _____

One ten and two units.   [ ]   _____

Three tens and three units.   [ ]   _____

Seven tens and eight units.   [ ]   _____

Nine tens and no units.   [ ]   _____

Five tens and seven units.   [ ]   _____

Can you add these sums quickly?

```
   t. u.        t. u.        t. u.        t. u.
   3 6          4 2          7 7          3 5
 + 1 4        + 2 8        + 1 4        + 3 5
 _____      _____      _____      _____


   t. u.        t. u.        t. u.        t. u.
   2 7          5 2          1 2          5 8
 + 1 9        + 3 8        + 2 9        + 3 2
 _____      _____      _____      _____
```

Draw an arrow from the star to the sum above which tells this story in numbers.

✳   Twenty-seven cows were grazing
      in a field when the farmer
      brought in nineteen horses.
      There was now a total of
      forty-six animals in the field.

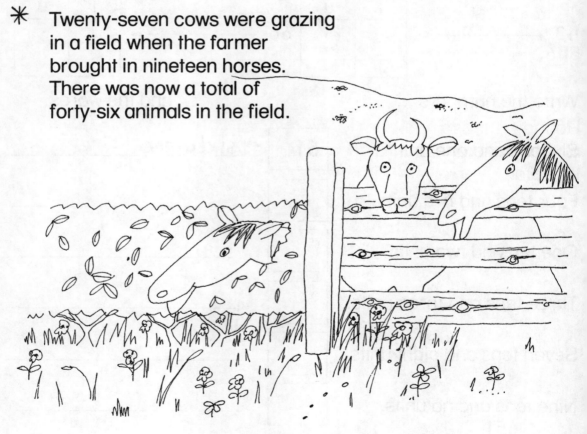

Read the numbers aloud, then write how many hundreds, tens and units there are in each.

146 ⟶ _one hundred, four tens and six units_

284 ⟶ _____

697 ⟶ _____

401 ⟶ _____

506 ⟶ _____

Round off these numbers to the <u>nearest 100</u>, then write the rounded off number. Total each of the four columns and write in the total.

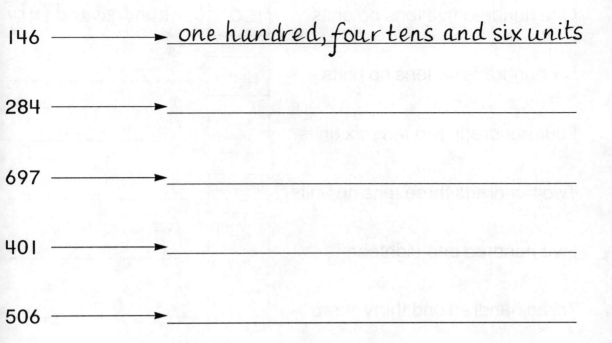

802 ⟶ 800   287

199   520

450   391

348   111

651   835

Total ____   ____   ____   ____

Can you write these numbers in figures and words?

One hundred five tens no units | 150 | _One hundred and fifty_

Six hundreds no tens no units | | _____

Four hundreds two tens six units | | _____

Two hundreds three tens no units | | _____

Five hundred and eighteen | | _____

Three hundred and thirty-three | | _____

Add numbers, read them aloud first, then read the completed sum.

502 and 214 ⟶

333 and 444 ⟶

471 and 518 ⟶

623 and 276 ⟶

Write your answers in a sentence.

How much shorter is the rope than the ladder?

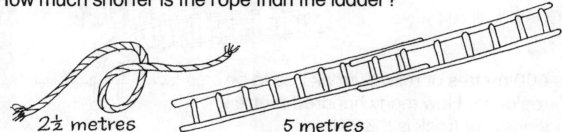

2½ metres   5 metres

By how many kilograms is Paul heavier than Rosie?

How many litres more does Mumtaz's tank hold than James's?

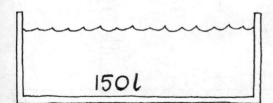 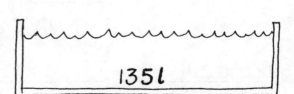

150 l   135 l

How much later did Ben arrive than Joy?

Read the question aloud before you calculate your answer, then write your answer in a sentence. Colour the pictures.

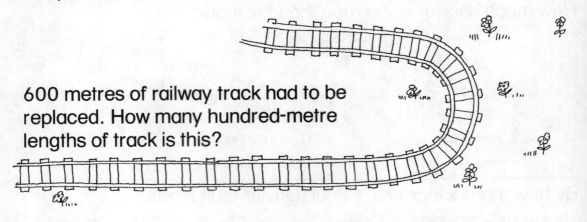

600 metres of railway track had to be replaced. How many hundred-metre lengths of track is this?

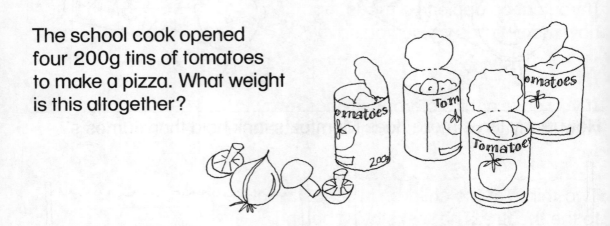

The school cook opened four 200g tins of tomatoes to make a pizza. What weight is this altogether?

There were sixteen pairs of shoes left in the sale. How many shoes is this altogether?

Make a fraction frame like the one on page 16, but this time use only three matchboxes to make one whole one.

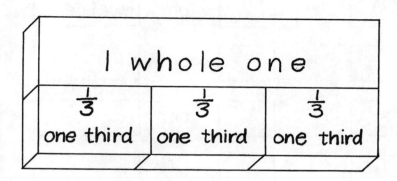

Use your frame to help you to answer the questions.

If you cut an apple into thirds,
how many thirds would you have?

If you gave a third of your savings away,
what fraction of your savings would be left?

Two-thirds of the children in school went
to the theatre. The rest stayed behind.
What fraction of the children stayed behind?

Colour the labelled areas of the circles.

 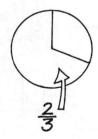  

$\frac{1}{3}$ $\frac{2}{3}$ I whole circle or $\frac{3}{3}$

Write the answers in the empty boxes.

$\frac{1}{3}$ of 36 = | 36 ÷ ③ | = | 12 | or | twelve |

$\frac{1}{4}$ of 20 = | | = | | or | |

$\frac{1}{2}$ of 10 = | | = | | or | |

$\frac{1}{3}$ of 18 = | | = | | or | |

$\frac{1}{2}$ of 24 = | | = | | or | |

$\frac{1}{4}$ of 28 = | | = | | or | |

$\frac{1}{2}$ of 30 = | | = | | or | |

$\frac{1}{3}$ of 30 = | | = | | or | |

$\frac{1}{4}$ of 8 = | | = | | or | |

$\frac{1}{2}$ of 100 = | | = | | or | |

The dotted section shows a missing piece. Which fraction of each shape is missing?

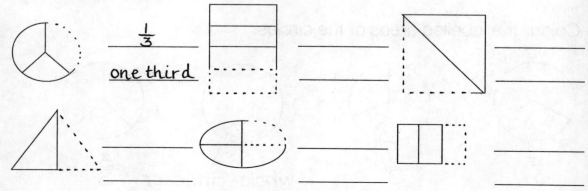

$\frac{1}{3}$

one third